THE BEST OF

C000059928

2000

'...And the Colonel gave me this one for having lovely eyes'

MATTHEW PRITCHETT studied at St Martin's School of Art in London and first saw himself published in the *New Statesman* during one of its rare lapses from high seriousness. He has been *The Daily Telegraph's* front-page pocket cartoonist since 1988. In 1995, 1996 and 1999 he was the winner of the Cartoon Arts Trust Award, in 1991 he was 'What the Papers Say' Cartoonist of the Year and in 1996, 1998 and 2000 he was *UK Press Gazette* Cartoonist of the Year.

The Daily Telegraph

THE BEST OF

2000

'Mowing the lawn
isn't "playing God"'

ORION

Orion Books
A division of the Orion Publishing Group Ltd
Orion House
5 Upper St Martin's Lane
London WC2H 9EA

First published by Orion Books in 2000

The right of Matthew Pritchett to be identified as the
author of this work has been asserted by him in accordance
with the Copyright, Designs and Patents Act, 1988

A CIP catalogue record for this book
is available from the British Library

ISBN 0 75283 765 6

Printed and bound in Great Britain by
The Guernsey Press Co. Ltd, Guernsey, C. I.

THE BEST OF

The Countryside

'Go past the derelict farm, turn right at the boarded-up post office and it's opposite the closed-down Barclays'

The Countryside

'*LOOK! A rural post office*'

The Countryside

Health Scares

Health Scares

Mayor for London

'I decided not to stand for Mayor of London because of my controversial past'

Mayor for London

'If you were any judge of character you wouldn't have married me in the first place'

Out with Archer . . .

'I said we should reinstate Norris, but take down the mistletoe'

. . . in with Norris and his complicated love-life

Mayor for London

'So the candidates for London mayor are: Lefty, Gloomy, Hopeless, Randy…'

MILLBANK TOWER

'Both Frank Dobson's supporters are stuck in the lift'

Mayor for London

'Oh no, the foxes have been at the dustbins again'

Political Questions

'Heckling the Prime Minister is one thing, but I don't agree with Cecily that we should blow up Hammersmith Bridge'

Political Questions

'I'm drinking to forget
my PIN number'

Political Questions

Jack Straw lets Tyson in . . .

'As a gesture of protest I sent Pinochet's luggage to Spain'

. . . and sends Pinochet home

Political Questions

'Be careful, it might lurch to the right at any moment'

Portillo revisits his Cambridge days

Political Questions

'If you look way, way down,
you can almost see the euro'

'I never realised sterling
was quite so strong'

Political Questions

'I must warn you, your views on the single currency are testing my loyalty to the limit'

'Break off all links with the Austrian ambassador'

Political Questions

'I mean, can you name three famous British Lib-Dem leadership contenders?'

'Getting warmer...no, cold...even colder...'

Political Questions

'If you wish to attack Hague, press one, if you wish to attack Major, press two...'

Banking Matters

Cashpoint charges instigated . . .   . . . and then abandoned

Banking Matters

Banking Matters

The Sporting Life

The two biggest sports signings of the year

The Sporting Life

'It would be wonderful to learn that, all these years, England have been losing on purpose'

Cricket scandals . . .

. . . as England footballers show how to lose properly. . .

The Sporting Life

'Bad dog! I'm going to take away your passport'

... and then there are the fans

The French

Another lorry strike . . .

. . . and storms

Pregnancy Young and Old

Pregnancy Young and Old

'I said, WE'RE GOING TO BE HEARING THE PATTER OF TINY FEET!'

'I wanted to concentrate on my career, so I've had my eggs poached'

The Scientific Age

'I've plotted the whole genetic code, but women are still a mystery to me'

The Health Service

'He swallowed the NHS questionnaire'

'Say aarh…'

The Health Service

'I still drink and smoke, but I've completely cut out the vitamin tablets'

Worries about
vitamin tablets . . .

. . . and incompetent doctors

The Health Service

'You'd never believe the
tales I could tell you
about NHS waiting lists'

The Internet

The Internet

'It says computer hackers have been reading our e-mail messages'

'He didn't compete at Crufts; he was too busy setting up his internet company'

The Internet

'INTERNET SHARES!'

What goes up . . .

'He only bought the computer
so he could watch internet
shares going down'

. . . must come down

Dunkirk Spirit

'I've come to take you to the
Dunkirk anniversary celebrations'

Motoring On

'You can have leather seats, air conditioning, and for a little extra, the whole company'

Motoring On

'For you, Tommy,
car production is over'

'Now I'm going to break it up
and sell off the parts'

Motoring On

'To me, Britishness is all about cricket, warm beer and an extra £3,000 on a Ford Fiesta'

'I hadn't noticed that speed hump before'

Motoring On

'It's cheaper than parking it'

'From here we continue our journey on foot'

Motoring On

'Mum, Dad, come quickly –
John Prescott is walking'

'It was just used by a
deputy PM to pop out and
make anti-car speeches'

Motoring On

'I'm arresting you for conspiracy to exceed the speed limit'

End of the Peers Show

'Aren't you going about constitutional reform in a rather reckless way, Mr Fawkes?'

End of the Peers Show

'You're meek and pliable, why aren't you a peer?'

'Don't just mope about — take a trip to the east wing or something'

The Millennium

'Tonight mustn't be just another disappointment — it should be the biggest anti-climax of our entire lives'

New Year's Eve . . .

The Millennium

'Well, thank goodness our computer wasn't affected'

'The Millennium bug wiped out all my New Year resolutions'

. . . January 1st

The Millennium

Horizontal wheel . . .

. . . and a bouncy bridge

The Millennium

'I never thought I'd say this, but the Dome is bringing me an enormous amount of pleasure'

The Armed Forces

'The only thing that stops
me leaving is the fear that
someone will kiss me goodbye'

The Armed Forces

The Blair Family

'If this is about Cherie Blair,
we know already'

The Blair Family

Law and Order

'Help me push this car into another police area'

Law and Order

'Come out with your hands up –
you're surrounded by
5,000 extra police'

Lack of police . . .

'I thought your mother was
about to steal an ashtray'

. . . raises issues
of self-defence . . .

Law and Order

'Daddy, what did you do in the Cenotaph riot?'

'When do we get to torch a police van?'

. . . as people riot for a cause

Oxford

'The neighbours' son got into Oxford – I always suspected they were lower class'

Oxford Entrance sparks class war

Oxford

'While the Government is on the subject of foxes, I didn't get into Oxford either'

'Congratulations, you've just won a scholarship to Oxford'

Oxford

'Our family motto is,
"Rejected by Oxford"'

'They say this ghastly class war
should be over by Christmas'

Back to Work

'No, I'm not in work... I'm on my way to a fancy dress party'

'Hello, luv, I'm on the trainee programme'

And Finally . . .

'Mum, hold all my calls
for the next ten years'

And Finally . . .

And Finally . . .

Moon eclipses sun . . .

. . . as Philip's foot eclipses mouth

And Finally . . .

'I'm arresting you for attempting to forge a Turner prize work of art'

'I knew the Cenotaph was vandalised, but you should see what they've done in there'

And Finally . . .

Spies are forgetful . . .

. . . Granny does a better job

And Finally . . .

'No quarantine — or he gets it'

When is a hostage not a hostage . . .

And Finally . . .

'How much for this?'

Difficulties on the High Street

And Finally . . .

Oscar night

Missing Mars probe

And Finally . . .

'We have a cottage up north
so the children can see the
poverty at weekends'

'Are you friends of the bride or
of the groom's first wife?'

North–South divide

And Finally . . .

And Finally . . .

And Finally . . .

'I've merged with
an internet company'

And Finally . . .

'Cheer up, mate, there are plenty more fish in the... well, cheer up anyway'

Fishing and catamarans in crisis

And Finally . . .

'This cat that's stuck up the tree;
it's not black, female or gay is it?'

Fire Service accused of
prejudice

'I heard you complaining
about the new licence fee'

And Finally . . .

'*Are you a day boy or a boarder?*'

'*This airline food is FANTASTIC*'

And Finally . . .

And Finally . . .

'The bookshop had sold out, so I stole this one from a child'